Editor: Laura Neutzling
Art Direction: Ron Eddy
Layout: Tod Carter
Illustration: Tod Carter

Published by Big Idea Entertainment, LLC. 320 Billingsly Court, Suite 30, Franklin, TN 37067

Printed in the U.S.A.

ISBN: 978-7-60587-416-6

VeggieTales®

Pa Grape's Shapes

by Phil Vischer

This is Pa Grape. He loves the outdoors!

He loves what God made —

all the mountains and shores!

He'd like to go visit the stuff he admires.

But look! His old car doesn't have any tires!

This is Pa Grape and the thing with the screen
Is his Robo 2000 New Tire Machine!
"It's really quite easy," says dear old Pa Grape;
"To get a new tire, just pick out a shape!"

"But I can't remember

— oh, dearie! Oh, me!

What shape does a tire for my car need to be?"

"Maybe a triangle! That ought to work!"
And the box springs to life
with a groan and a jerk —

And spits out a tire not too
big, not too small,
That just sits on the ground
— without rolling at all.

"Oh, dear," says the grape. "That's not good,
that's not good!
A tire should be rolling!
I know that it should!"

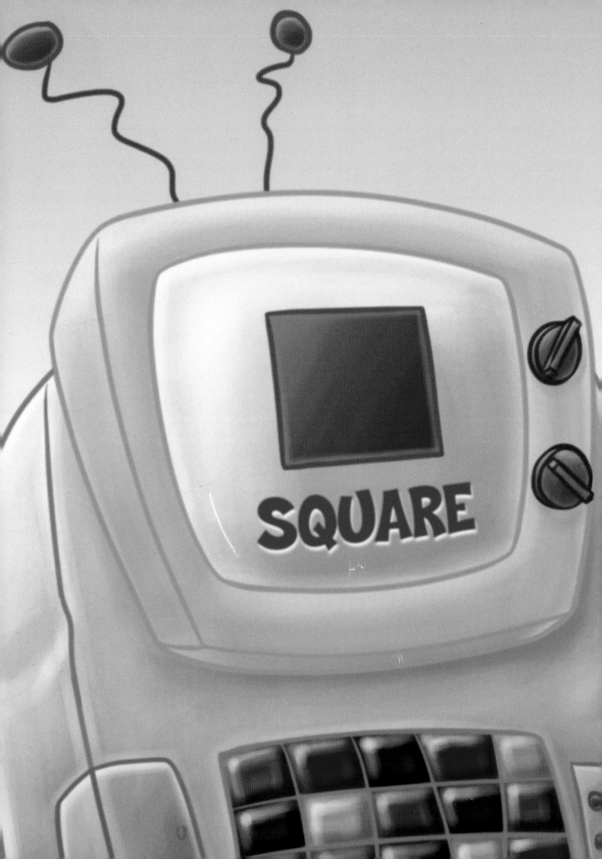

"Let's try a square! Oh, that's a nice shape! I think it's just right for my car," says Pa Grape.

The square hits the ground with a big, heavy thud. But roll it does not. Pa yells out, "What a dud!"

"I'll try a rectangle, just to be fair."

But it doesn't roll any more than the square!

"Here's an idea — I'd bet my new sweater!
Maybe a shape that is round will roll better!"

So Pa tries a crescent.

"The back part is round!"

But once it rolls over,
it sticks in the ground!

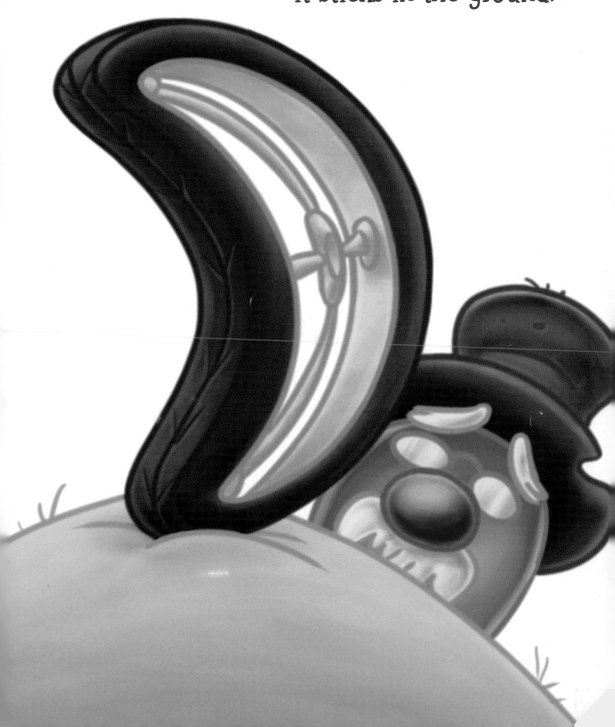

"Maybe an oval! It's round all the way!"

And out pop four ovals.
"They're rolling! Hurray!

I guess if it rolls it just might

do the trick —

But that wibblin' and wobblin'

will make us all sick!"

Now, here's a circle. The very last shape.

"It looks quite a bit like a ball," says Pa Grape.

"Hey! Balls are good rollers,
   I know that it's true!
So maybe a circle will roll nicely, too!"

At last the new tire appears
on the ramp.
It looks like a dream, and it
rolls like a champ!

"It's perfect!" cries Pa.

"Oh, so smooth and so round!

The tire for my car I have finally found!"

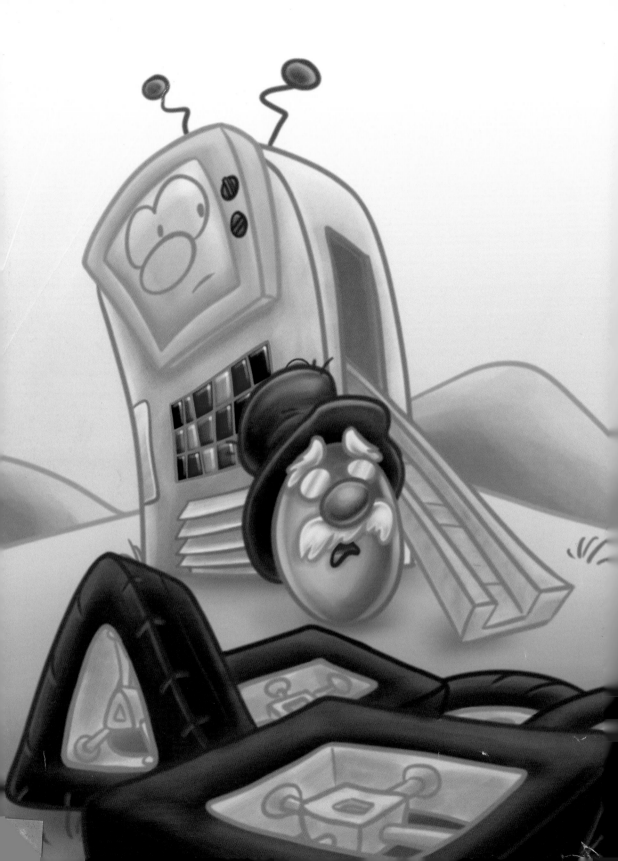

"Only one thing left to find now, I guess...
I need a good friend to help
clean up this mess!"

READ AND LEARN WITH BOB & LARRY

This series of Veggiecational Books is designed to help kids learn their letters, numbers, shapes, time and colors! Bob & Larry lead the way with great stories that help preschool kids with their educational basics in a fun and engaging way!

28 page Hardcover books measuring 7" by 9"

A Veggiecational Book about NUMBERS
VeggieTales
How Many Veggies?
by Phil Vischer

A Veggiecational Book about LETTERS
VeggieTales
Bob and Larry's ABC's
by Phil Vischer

A Veggiecational Book about COLORS
VeggieTales
Junior's Colors
by Phil Vischer

A Veggiecational Book about SHAPES
VeggieTales
Pa Grape's Shapes
by Phil Vischer

A Veggiecational Book about TIME
VeggieTales
Time for Tom
by Phil Vischer